Wild F of Spain

by

CLIVE INNES

COCKATRICE PUBLISHING LTD
Whitchurch, Hampshire, England

First published 1987
by Cockatrice Publishing Ltd.
Whitchurch, Hampshire RG28 7LN

© Cockatrice Publishing Ltd. 1987

British Library Cataloguing in Publication Data
Innes, Clive
    Wild Flowers of Spain
    1. Wild Flowers — Spain
    I. Title
    582' .13'0946   QK329

ISBN   1   870353   02   1.

Photographs by the author,
    J. Flack and L. Henslow

Printed in England

INTRODUCTION

This third booklet provides even further species of plants to be found on the Spanish mainland. A few have been included which are from other parts of the world, but have become naturalised in Spain, and in some instances are more outstanding than some of the native species.

It is anticipated that further booklets will be made available in the months ahead. There remain numerous plants deserving inclusion – with many of these they are 'names only' – colour photographs having never, to date, been published. It is hoped that wild plants from more northerly parts of the country will be depicted, because it is a fact, that what are to be discovered in the Mediterranean region are not found in central and northerly areas of the country.

More and more people find endless pleasure in roaming the country-side – and if one thing is irrefutable, it is that to wander over so much of the beautiful and unspoilt Spanish countryside will afford continual interest with its array of wild flowers. Whatever month of the year you may travel, interesting and colourful plants will be seen, and to the plant enthusiast these make a visit to such a lovely country even more worthwhile.

May you enjoy these booklets for indeed they are intended to eventually cover as much of the flora of Spain as possible.

It is often quoted that Spain has so much to offer its visitors and residents – but nothing excels the beauty and attraction of its flowering country-side.

Clive Innes

AGAVE americana L. (Agavaceae)

Common name — *Century Plant*

This species from N. America has become exceedingly well distributed throughout Spain during the past 200 years or so. It has acquired its common name due to the incorrect idea that it did not produce its flowers until it was 100 years old – this is, of course, a fallacy. It is a giant rosette-forming plant which is very much in evidence in the south of the country – and a feature on many a landscape.

The rosette consists of 20-30 stiff projecting bluish-green leaves, often to nearly 2m in length and 30cm or so wide near the base. There is a terminal spine at the tip of the partially inrolled leaves, blackish-brown in colour – the leaf margins decidedly crenate-dentate. The inflorescence is capable of reaching 6m or even more in length and carried about 25 short branches bearing large greenish-yellow or yellowish flowers each about 9cm long. The plant dies after flowering, but seems to always produce many offsets to replace the parent! Flowering mainly June to September, then it freely produces seeds.

ALLIUM neopolitanum Cyr.   (Alliaceae)

Common name — *Naples Garlic*

It has a widespread distribution throughout the Mediterranean region and is to be discovered in many parts of southern Spain growing in stony, rocky areas as well as in fields and olive groves. A bulbous plant, originally included within *Liliaceae*, which develops a wide spreading head of beautiful flowers.

Plants grow to 35-40cm when in bloom – stems are somewhat 3-angled. Leaves only few in number, usually 2-3, partially sheathing the stem – flattish, 1-2cm wide. Flowers are star-shaped or cup-shaped, carried on long stalks – pure white in colour, and as many as 20-30 or more comprising an umbel. Each flower about 2cm across – the whole head of flowers 6-9cm diameter subtended by a papery bract. There is also a variety of the species, commonly known as *A. cowanii* which is a more robust plant.

Flowers can be seen from March through to June or early July.

ANAGALLIS monelli L. (Primulaceae)
Common name — *Shrubby Pimpernel*

This is also known as *A. linifolia* – a suitable title in view of its very slender leaves. A low-growing plant, made very distinctive because of its vivid flowers. A perennial species, native to both sides of the Mediterranean – to be discovered in shrubby areas, pinewoods, grasslands and rocky places, often just above high-tide mark!

Leaves are linear-lanceolate, pointed and set opposite along the many slender branches – leaves are about 1cm long and only about 1mm wide. Flowers are a startlingly deep blue with a purplish centre, each to about 2cm across – but the size can vary – in fact a *subspecies linifolia* is recorded, but whether or not this is justified is in doubt as only the flower size appears slightly different. The flower stalks are from 2-4cm long, and carrying what are possibly the largest flowers of all the European species of the genus.

Flowering from February until late October.

ARISTOLOCHIA baetica L. (Aristolochiaceae)

Common name — *Birthwort*

This is one of the more extraordinary plants to be discovered in the south of the country. A climbing species – evergreen – to be found in low scrub areas or on low hillsides, especially dry parts of the Mediterranean region, particularly in the Provinces of Almeria, Malaga and Granada.

This long stemmed climber can reach well over 2m in length – the stems are firm, pale-green with leaves set at intervals along their length – leaves have stalks shorter than those of the flowers – glaucous, slightly leathery, hairless, cordate with pointed tips and pronounced basal lobes. Flowers are borne from the leaf axils – long-stalked, the corolla tube strongly curved with deep brownish-maroon, or very frequently, a blackish-purple trumpet which is slightly hairy on the inner surface, 4-6cm in total length. The fruits which follow are berry-like in shape. They can be seen in flower from April to June.

ARISTOLOCHIA sempervirens L.   (Aristolochiaceae)

Common name — *Pipe Vine*

This peculiar climbing plant is also known as *A. altissima* Desf. The distribution is quite widespread around the whole Mediterranean region. It grows in fairly shaded areas, especially in the Province of Malaga, more so on lower ground in dryish parts along with bushy shrubs and trees.

A rampant climber with elongated stems and somewhat rounded, lobed leaves, pointed at the tips, 6-8cm long and about 5cm across, smooth-edged, bright green in colour. Flowers are decidedly curved, funnel-shaped – a pale maroon swollen tube with a corolla of greenish-yellow, hairy on the margins, and a lip which is slightly oblique – carried on short stalks from the leaf axils.

Flowers are said to appear from January through to June, but this much depends upon habitat – that depicted was photographed in April.

ASTERISCUS maritimus (L.) Less.   (Compositae)

Common name — *Sea Asteriscus*

This is also known as *Odontospermum*. A mat-forming perennial usually encountered near the Mediterranean coastline amongst rocks quite close to the sea or on inland barren country in very stony ground.

It is really a most pleasing shrublet with a woody base from which arise many softer stems carrying very rough, hairy spatulate leaves which form in clusters at ground level. Flowers are a rich deep yellow, very similar to the common Marigold and completely subtended by bright leaf-like bracts, borne terminally on short hairy stems. Each flower-head about 4cm across with numerous ray and disk florets which glisten in the Spanish sunshine. A feature of the ray florets are the slightly toothed tips.

Flowering time starts in early spring – from early March and continuing until the latter part of June.

ASTRAGALUS glaux L. (Leguminosae)

Common name — *Purple Milk-Vetch*

A perennial plant of robust habit which, when in full growth, becomes densely clothed with numerous leaves and clusters of flowers. It seems to frequent dry grassy areas or low hillside pastures throughout central, southern and very rarely in northern parts of Spain.

Plants are clump forming to about 30cm across – many semi-erect branches bearing pinnate leaves comprised of 12-15 narrowly oblong leaflets – smooth on upper surface but slightly hairy on the underside. Flowers are a bright purple in colour, each about 1cm long carried in clusters at the terminal ends of rather short stalks – the calyx is about 5mm long which is toothed around the tip. This is quite a colourful species – remaining attractive even after flowering when the fruits form, each 6-8mm, covered with small whitish hairs and a short hooked tip.

A summer flowering species, from June through to early September.

11

CARLINA acaulis L.   (Compositae)

Common name — *Stemless Carline Thistle*

This is a perennial plant, generally low-growing, and rather variable. It is quite widespread in the Pyrenees, but is also known elsewhere including Britain – and it is probably the varying habitats which cause slight differences in the flower colourings. It is found in grassy places or in open woodland – generally in full sun and in calcareous soil.

One of the less vicious thistles – the leaves are widely spreading, deeply lobed, stiff, the margins with small spiny teeth – generally pale to deep green and formed into a fairly regular but sparsely-leaved rosette. Flowers are solitary, 10-15cm across – the outer involucral bracts resemble narrow, slender leaves – silvery-white, yellowish-white – sometimes pinkish or pale brown. The inner bracts slender, pointed, yellowish or whitish – the florets white, or rarely yellow. Flowers are stemless or with only a very brief stalk.

Flowering from late May until September.

CARPOBROTUS acinaciformis (L.)L.Bol.

(Mesembryanthemaceae)

Common name — *Red Hottentot Fig*

This is of South African origin which has become naturalised in many parts of Spain, particularly the Mediterranean region. A succulent plant of spreading habit found in plenty near or in the sand on the sea-shore.

Stems are elongated to well over 1m in length, angular and tough – any branches are quite short. Leaves are fleshy, slightly greyish-green or fresh-green, about 9cm long, 1cm wide – more or less triangular in cross-section, showing a deciding keel which is generally rough. They are set opposite and united at the base. Flowers are large, about 12cm across, mostly opening to the full in the afternoon – brilliant crimson-purple – the creamy-yellow of the pollen providing an attractive centre. They are always borne singly.

Flowering is from April to July, followed by the fruits which are edible.

CENTRANTHUS ruber (L.) DC.　　　　　　　(Leguminosae)

Common name — *Red Valerian*

A bushy-based perennial species which has become widely naturalised in many parts of Europe, including Britain. Its origin is very much the Mediterranean region – but it can be observed in many parts of Spain from the north to the south, growing in calcareous rocky places on mountains and lower hillsides.

This tufted plant has several very erect, robust stems 60-80cm tall. Leaves are set in opposite pairs, ovate to lanceolate, about 10cm long, the margins entire except those towards the tips of the stems being toothed and stalkless. Individual flowers are tubular in shape, about 1cm long with a slender spur – reddish in colour, but occasionally white or pink flowers. These are borne in terminal panicles and very sweetly scented. It is also of interest that the rootstock, which is very thick, is quite fragrant. Flowering early March until September.

CIRSIUM eriophorum (L.) Scop. (Compositae)

Common name — *Woolly Thistle*

Most thistles have an attraction – and this is no exception. A sturdy, robust species which quickly captures the eye with its magnificent head of flowers. Its habitat is limited to much of central and southern Spain, also seen in France – it frequents both high and low ground, but especially on the lower mountain slopes in stony areas to about 150m altitude, near to the Mediterranean coatline.

An erect, stout stem to 45cm or more high which carries large, viciously-spined leaves – these having two rows of spiny lobes – one row pointing erect, the other down-pointing, and with pointed tips. The flower-head is large, broad, rich-reddish-purple in colour – the involucral bracts are spine-tipped and have cobweb-like hairs almost totally covering them.

Even in the bud stage they are attractive, but the flowers display the plant to best advantage and can be seen during July and August.

CORIS monspeliensis L.   (Primulaceae)

Common name — *Coris*

A stiff, woody-based, branching species which is generally of annual growth, although in some instances it has proved to be perennial. It is found on hillsides in stony terrain – also known in sandy areas near to the Mediterranean coast.

Stems are to about 20-25cm long, more or less erect. Leaves are very small, narrow, tough, hairless and bluntly tipped and usually spiny at the base – dull greyish-green in colour and very reminiscent of certain species of Thyme. A much branching species each carrying a terminal head of bloom. Flowers are 2-lipped – 3 upper petals and 2 lower – pinkish-lilac in colour with reddish-purple sepals. Calyx somewhat bell-shaped, with two rows of very small teeth – the five lobes triangular, sometimes with black dots.

Flowering is principally between April and July – but in maritime sands this often extends into August.

CYNOGLOSSUM cheirifolium L.   (Boraginaceae)

Common name — *Hound's Tongue*

This is a biennial plant which grows a matter of 30-45cm tall, sometimes even taller. One of several species of the genus, all of European origin. Plants are found mostly in the south of Spain, from low ground to about 200m altitude, and they can be frequently encountered near to the Mediterranean coastline in rocky terrain or similarly dry places.

The stem is erect, covered with a whitish coating of minute soft hairs, like felt. Leaves are lanceolate in shape, also white-felted on both surfaces – and they are stalkless, set alternate along the length of the stem. Flowers are in terminal clusters – reddish-purple which gradually change to a deeper shade of purple – or often blue – the corolla is about 6-8mm across, hairless, the corolla tube a little longer. The seed capsules – nutlets as they are termed – are about 7mm wide, covered with spine-like projections, slightly concave or flat. Flowering period is from April through to late June.

CYNOGLOSSUM creticum Miller   (Boraginaceae)

Common name — *Blue Hound's Tongue*

A biennial plant with very erect stems often attaining about 40cm tall. It frequents shady places, and more often that not in quite stony ground in scrub and sparsely wooded areas. Principally found in the Mediterranean region, from low ground to more rocky hillsides at about 200m.

Stems are sturdy and covered with numerous whitish hairs – the leaves are also greyish or whitish hairy on both surfaces, giving a velvety effect – the basal leaves are lanceolate, those towards the upper part of the stem are somewhat blunted at the tips and clasp the stem. Flowers are pale blue and finely veined with purple, to about 1cm across. These are in terminal clusters – the seed capsules (nutlets) have no raised edges, but the convex 'face' is covered with very short spines.

Flowering from March to June.

DACTYLORHIZA sambucina (L.) Soó   (Orchidaceae)

Common name — *Elder-flowered Orchid*

The rootstock is tuberous and this in the form of two lobes (as in *Orchis*). It is usually associated with more eastern parts of the Mediterranean coast, but it also occurs in central parts of Spain in mountain pastures and similar grassy places or open woodland to altitudes of up to 2000m – fairly common in the Provinces of Zaragoza and Huesca.

Plants are to about 30cm tall, often much shorter, the stem either green but more frequently somewhat brownish-purple. Leaves are few, these are fresh-green, unspotted, widely lanceolate in shape – those nearer the flower spike are narrower. Bracts purplish. Flowers form a dense, compact spike – mostly reddish with a deeper red or purplish-red lip, or pale yellow with faint purplish dots on the lip. Lip 3-lobed, 6-7mm long. The hood consists of the central sepal and the petals – the lateral sepals are upward-facing. The spur is conical, quite firm and downward pointing. Flowering March to late June.

DATURA stramonium L. (Solanaceae)

Common name — *Thorn Apple*

An erect, sturdy branching species which is possibly not native to Europe, but is now quite widespread in its distribution – even to Britain. It is considered an annual, growing from 45cm to 100cm tall. It is, however, poisonous, containing dangerous alkaloids. It is frequently seen along the Mediterranean coastline – in cultivated and uncultivated areas alike – more often in open country.

An erect plant with robust, somewhat fleshy stems, usually with 1-2 or more branches. Leaves dark-green, to about 20cm long, with undulating margins and partially indented, and these bedeck the upper part of the plant. Flowers more or less erect, 8-10cm long – the funnel-shaped corolla usually white, the tips often twisted and pointed – the 5-lobed calyx to about 4cm long, pale-green or whitish, 5-angled with small teeth. These are followed by oval fruits 4-5cm long.

In general flowers can be seen between mid-April to mid-September.

EUPHORBIA cyparissias L.   (Euphorbiaceae)

Common name — *Cypress Spurge*

This is a rhizomatous species which occurs in hilly country, usually in calcareous soil, and produces short bright-green, slender branches with equally slender and green leaves – very much resembling a juvenile fir-tree. It abounds principally in the Pyrenees – from the slopes leading up to Andorra to more coastal regions.

It is very much a spreading plant and is deciduous throughout the coldest months of the year. Flowering stems can be from 30-50cm long producing terminal heads of flowers consisting of 10 or more rays enclosed within kidney-shaped bracts – the flowers at first yellowish, but gradually turning to a deep reddish-brown. An attractive, but invasive plant which has become quite popular in cultivation.

This is a spring-flowering plant and likely to be seen at its best from mid-April until late in June.

21

FRITILLARIA lusitanica Wikstr.   (Liliaceae)

Common name — *Spanish Fritillary*

This is an extremely variable species in respect to colour, although otherwise the characteristics remain more or less constant. A bulbous plant also known as *F. hispanica*, to be found at varying altitudes and habitats – mostly in low mountainous country in stony ground amongst scrub in southern, central and eastern districts of Spain – the accompanying picture was taken on the lower slopes of Bernia – Alicante Province, 300-400m altitude.

This is generally a short to medium sized plant, mostly around 15-30cm tall. The leaves are greyish-green, 7-9 in number, set alternate, linear-lanceolate, to 1cm wide. Flowers are bell-shaped, 2-3cm long and about the same across – slightly flared at the tips of the petals – borne solitary or 2-3 together – brownish-red or purplish sometimes with green being in evidence in a band along the centre of each tepal – and this may sometimes be yellowish – the style 3-lobed. Flowers can be seen from early March through to late May.

GAGEA arvensis (Pers.) Roem. & Schult.   (Liliaceae)

Common name — *Field Gagea*

This is one of a group of quite small lily-like bulbous plants, some species of which are so similar as to be difficult to determine – only minor characteristics help identify a species. This plant is associated with dryish fields and verges at altitudes to 1000m in southern regions of the country, especially in parts of Alicante and Malaga Provinces.

Plants vary from about 5cm to 15cm high, and the stems are minutely hairy. The foliage consists of just two basal, slender leaves about 3mm wide and 2-3 smaller leaves immediately below the head of flowers. Flowers appear towards the tips of the stems, up to 12 or more in a loose cluster, each flower about 1-1.5cm long. The principal colouring is yellow, but greenish on the outer surface – very star-like in shape, borne on hairy stalks.

Flowering is during the earlier part of the year – from mid-February and early March to well into May.

GENTIANA verna L. (Gentianaceae)

Common name — *Spring Gentian*

This very beautiful plant occurs in the south of Spain, being widespread in Sierra Nevada, and also known on the grassy slopes of the Pyrenees.

This is a really choice dwarf species – very low growing and forming a rather sparse 'mat'. It is said to have the deepest and most intense blue colouring of any of the species, including *G. acaulis*. Leaves are small, ovate to lanceolate, 1-2cm long, and develop into small rosettes of 6-10 leaves. The flower stalks can vary from 3-10cm long and appear from the centre of each rosette. From the tips of the stems are borne rich deep-blue flowers – just one to a stalk each about 2cm across, the outer colouring of the petals being greenish-blue – the five blue spreading lobes form a crowning feature to the slender cylindrical flower.

Flowers are to be seen from early March to well into August.

HELIANTHEMUM apenninum (L.) Miller   (Cistaceae)

Common name — *White Rockrose*

A low growing species which can be very variable in its flower colouring. It is a perennial and when developed into a substantial cluster, is most impressive. It grows on dry hills and in rocky places throughout much of Spain – principally in low scrub country.

A quite weak-stemmed plant which branches very freely, these invariably are semi-prostrate on the ground with only the flowering stems lifting their heads. Leaves can vary from greyish-white woolly to be more or less smooth and green – the margins are inrolled. Stipules very narrow and slender. Flowers are about 2cm across – generally pure white with a bright yellow centre – a pink form is also known, but this does not appear to frequent the Spanish mainland – flowers from towards the tips of the stems, the slightly drooping flower-buds lifting their heads as the flowers open.

Flowering freely between May and July.

HELLEBORUS foetidus L.   (Ranunculaceae)

Common name — *Stinking Hellebore*

This is usually more pleasantly called Christmas Rose – and is, of course, the species cultivated in Britain. If damaged, it does however have a strong smell which accounts for the common name ascribed. It is native of low hillsides and mountain slopes in the south of the country, mainly in rocky scrub areas – prevalent in the Province of Valencia and Albacete.

A bushy plant 30-75cm tall, with finger-shaped leaflets which are minutely toothed borne on the biennial stems. Flowers are cup-shaped, to about 3cm across, greenish-white with a distinctive red-dish-brown edging to the tips of the sepals – they are borne in clusters, the flowers having a drooping habit. A particular feature is the fact that the upper leaves are always paler than those *towards* the base of the stems – there are no actual basal leaves.

Flowering is from January to early April,

IRIS juncea Poir.   (Iridaceae)

Common name — *Rush Iris*

This is one of a number of species within the *Xiphium* group of *Iris* which have a bulbous rootstock. A fairly erect plant which in flower reaches 30-40cm high. It is native of southern and south-easterly parts of Spain, usually in rocky areas from 300-1500m altitudes, particularly in Provinces of Granada and Malaga.

Plants have long slender leaves only to about 3mm wide – firm, but slightly spreading. Flower stems bear 2 bright yellow flowers – beautifully scented – the falls have a very faint brownish veining towards the base and also on the short haft. The feature which primarily separates this from *I. xiphium* is the very long flower tube which is from 3.5-5cm in length. The flowers can differ in the yellow colouring and this has resulted in two or three varietal titles being established.

Flowering is for a somewhat restricted period – but from early May until mid-June they can be seen at their best.

LAVATERA arborea L.   (Malvaceae)

Common name — *Tree Mallow*

A large perennial species with stems often to 3m in length, developing almost tree-like proportions. It is fairly common in many parts of Spain, especially near the coasts where it grows among rocks and sand to altitudes to 250m.

Stems are robust, almost rounded, woody based and branching freely. Leaves are broadly cordate, very hairy, to about 20cm diameter, 5-9 lobed – the upper surface with minute star-like hairs, the under-surface greyish-white woolly. Flowers are reddish-purple in colour and veined with a deeper shade – to about 5cm across borne in clusters of several flowers near the tips of the stems. Petals are quite broad, obovate, slightly overlapping, each with a small deep purplish base. The fruits which follow are slightly ridged and rough.

Flowering is prolonged over a period from early April until September.

LAVATERA maritima Gouan   (Malvaceae)

Common name — *Sea Mallow*

This is a woody shrub with several branches, often attaining 120cm tall and 60cm wide. It has quite a widespread distribution throughout the whole Mediterranean region, and can be seen flourishing in dry rocky places near the sea and on calcareous rock-faces overlooking the sea at altitudes to about 150m.

A perennial species with whitish or greyish stems. Leaves are rounded and shallowly lobed and covered with minute soft whitish hairs. Flowers are the principal feature – pale pink or bluish-pink in colour, 3-4cm across, borne on short stalks, several to each stem. Flowers have a purplish-red throat, and set within the centre of this area are five green lobes with yellowish bases – appearing like 'eyes'. Fruits follow, these are hairless, but as they mature become black.

Period of flowering depends to some extent upon location – but in general they are to be seen between mid-February to mid-May.

LAVENDULA stoechas L.   (Labiatae)
  subsp. **pedunculata** (Miller) Samp.

Common name — *French Lavender*

This subspecies does not indicate the origin as suggested by the common name (see also Vol. 1, p.42). It is found only on the Spanish' mainland, generally in quite heavily wooded country on low hills and mountain slopes. An aromatic shrub which can attain 60cm or a little more in height, and invariably very compact with densely set branches, leaves – and flowers. Prevalent in the south of the country growing in calcareous soil.

Leaves are very similar to those of the species – greyish-green in colour, 1-4cm long, linear to oblong-lanceolate, and appearing more or less along the whole length of the numerous branches. Flowers are much brighter than those of the species, rich-purple or reddish-purple, borne terminally on the branches. The subtending bracts are similarly coloured – and this head of bracts and flowers is from 2-5cm long. Flowers can be seen from late February to late June.

LEUCANTHEMUM vulgare Lam.   (Compositae)

Common name — *Ox-eye-Daisy*

A perennial species which develops from a rhizomatous rootstock and forms into a branched shrublet to about 30-50cm tall. It is widespread throughout much of Spain, particularly from more central to southern regions – on hillsides, low mountain slopes and grassy, rocky areas – very much in evidence in the northerly parts of Alicante Province and neighbouring Albacete.

The basal leaves are more or less oval or spatulate, narrowing at the base – those on the upper part of the stem are more slender – narrowly lanceolate, partially indented along the margins or toothed. Flowers are terminally borne, 3-6cm across – the ray florets are white, strap-like – the centre disc consists of numerous yellow florets packed densely together, like a miniature 'cushion', each disc-floret being minutely tubular in shape.

The flowering season is primarily between May and September.

31

LUNARIA annua L. (Cruciferae)

Common name — *Honesty*

This well-known species needs no introduction – it is generally considered a biennial, unlike the similar *L. rediviva* which is perennial, and possibly more common in the wild. It is to be discovered from north to south of Spain, mostly at altitudes to about 250m – usually in moist areas on grassy, rocky slopes or along the wayside.

Plants 45-60cm tall, the stem robust and erect. Leaves are set in opposite pairs, each leaf to about 15cm long, somewhat heart-shaped and coarsely toothed – the upper leaves stalkless. Flowers are in the form of a terminal cluster, each 4-petalled flower about 2cm across – a rose-pink or reddish-purple in colour, rarely white. Fruits are almost circular in outline and become extremely thin when dry – about 3-6cm long. An exceptional item for dried flower arrangements.

Flowering is from April through to late June.

MEDICAGO marina L. (Leguminosae)

Common name — *Sea Medick*

An attractive sea-shore plant of spreading habit, invariably prostrate over the sands. It occurs throughout the Mediterranean area in southern Spain, growing just above high water mark on the shore.

Stems are slender, white felted rarely exceeding 15cm long, trailing and spreading to form quite large clusters. Leaves are pinnate, divided into 5-7 more or less obovate leaflets which are totally covered in minute white-woolly hairs – the leaflet margins are incurved. Flowers are bright yellow – 6-8mm long and appear in rounded heads of many flowers at the ends of the stems carried on short stalks. These are followed by coiled fruits in 3 spirals, with or without spines and covered with woolly hairs. Altogether quite a robust species and made very attractive because of the predominance of the white-woolly features.

Flowers are in evidence from April through to late June.

NICOTIANA glauca Graham   (Solanaceae)

Common name — *Tree Tobacco*

This is actually a native of N. Argentina but has become widely naturalised on waste ground and among rocks throughout much of the Mediterranean region. A shrub-like plant, often attaining 2-3m in height – only few branches, but these tend to be widely spreading. An evergreen plant – and likely to be found in flower throughout the year.

Leaves are tough and hairless, carried on a long stalk – ovate in shape, often to 25cm long. The flowers are bright yellow, 3-4.5cm long and about 5mm across at the tips, slightly hairy on the outer surface. The tubular-shaped calyx has 5 teeth, and this surrounds the fruit. The flowers are borne towards the tips of the branches in loose, somewhat pendent clusters.

Flowers are certainly seen at their best from May to September, although they are rarely out of bloom.

OLEA europaea L. (Oleaceae)

Common name — *Olive*

The cultivated Olive is a feature which is inescapable in the central and south of Spain – it is undoubtedly the cultivated form of the original wild species which still abounds, and currently named *subspecies oleaster* (Hoffm. & Link.) Fiori. There is some uncertainty as to the original habitat, but it seems probable it was the Middle East.

The Olive grows to a matter of 8-10m tall – the grey bark encompassing the trunk which is invariably gnarled, eventually, with age, developing a base of 45cm or more wide. Leaves are oblong-lanceolate, greyish-green on the upper surface, whitish below, set opposite along the branches. Flowers are whitish, borne in small clusters – the calyx with 4 teeth – the corolla with 4 widely spread lobes. Fruit at first green, becoming black.

Flowering is in late April to June, after which the fruits begin to form.

OPHRYS fusca Link   (Orchidaceae)
    subsp. **fusca** Nels.

Common name — *Sombre Bee Orchid/*
Brown Bee Orchid

There are a number of subspecies which vary very little one from the other. This is a perennial plant rarely exceeding 30cm tall when in flower. It is a widespread species along much of the Mediterranean region, frequenting rocky scrub areas and in sparse grasslands – and is very much in evidence in the low mountains and wooded areas near to the coast in Alicante and Malaga Provinces.

Leaves are both basal and stem – green in colour – the stem leaves slender, pointed at the tips, the basal more oblong-lanceolate. The spike carries 3-8 flowers – these have greenish sepals, occasionally more pinkish – the petals greenish-yellow and shorter than the sepals – the lip 3-lobed, about 1.5cm long, a velvety chocolate-brown or purplish-brown with a suggestion of a yellowish edge and bluish W-shaped reflections near the base. Flowering February until May.

OPHRYS scolopax Cav.   (Orchidaceae)
subsp. **scolopax** Nels.

Common name — *Woodcock Orchid*

A most variable species, some varieties of which are ́botanically recognised. They vary in height from 15-35cm – possibly one of the more frequently encountered orchids along the Mediterranean coastline – from quite low-lying stony, sparsely grassy areas to altitudes of about 150m – but generally in scrub or coarse-grass.

A very attractive plant with bright-green lance-shaped leaves both at the base and those sheathing the stem, but the latter are smaller, and pointed. Spikes carry 3 or more flowers – the sepals pink, occasionally pale-purplish, oblong in shape – the centre one erect – the petals of similar colouring, somewhat triangular and pointed. The lip oblong or almost rounded, 8-12mm or more long, reddish-brown with a series of lines in white or yellow resembling a shield. The tip often 'toothed'. There are also 2 basal swellings which may remain or elongate into very slender 'horns'. Flowering during April and May.

37

OPHRYS sphegodes Miller   (Orchidaceae)

Common name — *Early Spider Orchid*

This is a most variable species – the plant depicted does not totally conform to botanical descriptions – it might well be *subsp. atrata* – but probably only a variant of the type. It is associated with grassy, rocky places in calcareous soil, on low hillsides, often in clearings in scrub country. Fairly widespread on the hills in Alicante Province – plentiful on Montgo and Bernia.

A tuberous rooted species, rarely exceeding 45cm tall, generally much shorter. The green leaves are arranged in a basal rosette – these are oval-lanceolate, always blunt-tipped and slightly recurved. Spikes can carry 2-10 flowers – the petals greenish-purple or brownish-green, the sepals longer, mostly similarly coloured. The velvet-brown lip can be lobed or unlobed, about 1-1.2cm long, sometimes as much wide, with an 'H'-shaped speculum in lilac-blue or purple,.

Flowering season is mainly from mid-February to early May.

ORCHIS coriophora L.   (Orchidaceae)
subsp. **fragrans** Pollich

Common name — *Bug Orchid*

A fairly low growing species scarcely ever exceeding 40cm high when in bloom. The type species is less frequently encountered in Spain – and it smells of bugs! The subspecies, however, is more common and has the scent reminiscent of vanilla! It occurs right along the Mediterranean region of Spain, in moist, grassy places, usually in acid soil and at altitudes to about 1000m.

Leaves are long, narrow and pointed, sheathing the stem towards the tip – bright green in colour. Bracts are about 1cm long, lanceolate, 1-veined and becoming shorter towards the upper part of the stem. Flowers about 1cm long, assembled in short dense spikes – the hood is pointed, comprising the brownish-purple sepals and petals. The lip about 8mm with three lobes, the centre slightly larger, deep reddish-green or purplish-green. The spur 8-11mm long. Flowering from early April to June.

ORCHIS laxiflora Lam. (Orchidaceae)

Common name — *Loose-flowered Orchid*

A variable orchid – from 30-60cm or more tall when in flower. It frequents moist areas around much of the European Mediterranean – in the south of Spain, in grassy, marshy meadows or scrubland, near to streams and the like, at fairly low altitudes to about 100m.

Leaves are only few, 3-5, sometimes to 8 – narrowly-lanceolate and distinctly pointed, keeled and more or less erect – bluish-green on the underside, fresh green above, and they do not sheath the upper part of the stem. Flowers are borne on a loose spike – 6-20 to a spike – generally purplish-red in colour. The bracts are lance-shaped, suffused pinkish-purple, usually with 3-5 veins, these backing the 1.5-2cm long flowers. The two lateral sepals curve backwards, the upper sepal and the petals forming a hood. The lip 3-lobed, edges undulating – the centre lobe shorter than the outer lobes – altogether about 1cm long with purplish or whitish spots in the centre of the lip. Spur cylindrical, broad at the tip. Flowering from March to June.

ORNITHOGALUM umbellatum L.   (Liliaceae)

Common name — *Star of Bethlehem*

This is a very variable species, differing considerably according to its habitat. A bulbous plant which frequently, not always, produces a number of bulbils or offsets. It has quite a wide distribution, from low to high altitudes, even to 2000m. Plants can be seen in many parts of Spain, and quite common in central and southern hilly, grassy and stony areas.

Plants are only short, 8-30cm tall when in flower – leaves about 2mm wide, dark green with a whitish median line on the upper surface. The bulbils each produce a single, almost thread-like leaf, so that by flowering time, a small, compact colony is apparent. Flowers are set in a somewhat flattened-top raceme – from 3-15 or more – white with a green band on the back of each tepal – each flower star-like, 1.5cm or more across. The seed capsule is six-lobed and contains many seeds. Flowering is from April through to June.

OROBANCHE arenaria Borkh. (Orobanchaceae)

Common name — *Sand Broomrape*

This is one of the most fascinating of European parasitic plants – fascinating and extremely attractive. It is parasitic on species of the *Compositae* such as *Artemisia campestris* and other sea-shore plants. This species seems to have a fairly restricted distribution in the Province of Malaga, Granada and Almeria. The branching habit might well suggest that this is a form or variety of the species.

Stems are erect, fleshy, generally simple, but occasionally multi-branched, arising from basal tuberous swellings which are attached to the rootstock of the host plant. Stems are 15-30cm tall, about 3mm wide. Flowers occur from the tip to almost the base of the stem, bluish-purple in colour, 2.5-3cm long, each flower subtended by a brownish bract and two bracteoles – there is a paler tip to the lower lip which is minutely hairy as are also the anthers.

Flowers are at their best in late May or June.

OROBANCHE minor Sm. (Orobanchaceae)

Common name — *Lesser Broomrape*

This is one of the more variable of parasitic plants, and this variation seems to be dictated by which plants they find as 'hosts'. They are to be found on low growing species of the *Compositae* and *Leguminosae,* mainly on species of *Trifolium*, the clover family. They are widespread in Spain, often quite densely populating fields and meadows – it is also known in Britain.

Plants vary in height from 10cm to over 40cm – the flower-head is densely set with many small pale yellow flowers, often slightly suffused with purple near to the tips, and the petals veined in similar colour. Each flower 1-1.5cm long with a regularly curved tube – the upper lip forward-facing and a purplish-mauve stigma. Any pronounced colouring tends to be short-lived.

Flowering can be over quite a long period – they are frequently seen in March (when the above picture was taken) or often to late July.

PHLOMIS fruticosa L. (Labiatae)

Common name — *Jerusalem Sage*

This is possibly the most picturesque and attractive of the *Phlomis* – a beautiful shrubby plant, even before the flowers appear. The common name does not definitely define the habitat, although it is known in the Middle East – it has a widespread distribution in Spain, mainly in the Provinces bordering the Mediterranean where it is found in dry rocky areas.

It grows to a matter of 1m tall with branching stems which are white cottony-felted. The leaves are narrowly oval or elliptic, truncate at the base, greyish-white woolly on the under surface – a feature which quickly makes the plant recognisable! Flowers are each about 3cm long, golden-yellow, borne in a terminal head of 1-3, rarely 4 whorls – each with 20 or more flowers. The calyx has short teeth – and subtending each flower cluster are slightly oval bracts.

Flowers can be seen from late March until June or early July.

PLANTAGO coronopus L.   (Plantaginaceae)

Common name — *Buck's-Horn Plantain*

The Plantains are not necessarily among the most attractive of Spanish plants – but there are a few which deserve consideration. This can be discovered in many parts of the Mediterranean region, growing on wasteland, stony, uncultivated areas and very frequently on the sea-shore just above high water mark, in full sun.

It is a stemless species – the leaves are formed into a very attractive, symmetric rosette to 20cm or more in diameter. The leaves differ from most other species of the genus in having lobed leaves – these are deeply set – often the lobes are divided again into quite slender sections. All leaves lie completely flattened to form the dense rosette. Flower spikes are numerous – these appear from the base of the rosette and curve upwards round the circumference of the leaves – brownish-green in colour and bearing many very small yellowish-white flowers. Flowering is from late March to August, sometimes even later, dependent upon habitat.

PRIMULA veris L.   (Primulaceae)

Common name — *Cowslip*

A species which requires no introduction! It is certainly a British native, but also is found in many other parts of Europe, including the lower hillsides in the Pyrenees, particularly on the hilly slopes leading down from Andorra towards Lerida. It is more prevalent when the soil is calcareous – growing in both full sun and in sparsely wooded areas.

Plants are perennial – they grow to 10-20cm tall when in full bloom. Leaves are more or less arranged in a basal rosette – they are wrinkled, slightly recurved and undulating at the margins, generally ovate-lanceolate to elliptic, abruptly narrowing at the base, deep green in colour. Flowers are in a 1-sided umbel – slightly scented – the corolla deep yellow, the calyx greenish-yellow, short-pointed at the tips – 4-6 flowers to each terminal umbel, and inclined to be pendent.

Flowering from late March to June.

REICHARDIA tingitana (L.) Roth.   (Compositae)

Common name — *Mock Hawkbit*

A small genus of quite colourful plants, all from the Iberian Peninsula. This perennial species is possibly the most common – it is primarily in the south and east of Spain, where it is found in stony, sandy places or coarse grassy areas on low dry hillsides. It receives its common name due to the similarity between this and species of *Leontodon.*

Nearly all the leaves are basal, more or less in the form of a rosette. These are glaucous, and divided into a number of finely toothed lobes – the few lower stem leaves can be similar or smooth-edged, these clasping the stem. The flowering stalk is leafless, and this bears a solitary rich golden-yellow flower with a brownish-purple centre – each flower about 2.5cm across. The involucre bracts have a papery margin, and are arranged in a series of rows. An interesting feature of the species are the small white projections which cover much of the plant. Flowering is from May to July.

RICINUS communis L. (Euphorbiaceae)

Common name — *Castor Oil Plant*

This is one of the several tropical plants which have become naturalised in parts of Spain, particularly in the south of the country where it is very common. A sturdy shrub or tree-like plant of perennial growth to be found on waste-land and uncultivated ground.

It has large palmate leaves which are 5-7 lobed, deep rich-green in colour. Flowers are borne on a stout spike in dense erect clusters – reddish-orange – and these are either male or female, the male flowers being below the female. The fruit capsules which follow are large, covered with longish spines which, when ripened disclose several large smooth brownish seeds with a somewhat mottled surface. It is from these seeds that the medicinal oil is produced.

The flowering period proves to be uncertain, and much seems to depend upon location – but in general flowers and fruits appear almost throughout the year from February until late November.

SAXIFRAGA globulifera Desf.   (Saxifragaceae)

Common name — *Button Saxifrage*

This is very much a Spanish species, being found only on the rocky mountain slopes of Sierra de Ronda and Sierra Blanca. It has not seemingly found a popular place as a garden plant, but in its own surroundings is certainly an item of significance and charm. A mat-forming species which bedecks limestone rock-faces.

Leaves are semi-circular in outline and quite deeply lobed, densely set and spreading to form loose cushions in the rock crevices. Even in flower, it is, perhaps, not so spectacular as some other species – however, the short flowering stems, 7-12cm in length, each bear a number of small white flowers – possibly 3-7 to a stem – and these produce a glistening effect to the whole plant.

It is a late summer, early autumn flowerer, even although the buds form much earlier – and these are somewhat 'button'-shaped and very finely coated with minute hairs. An interesting species.

SAXIFRAGA oppositifolia L. (Saxifragaceae)

Common name — *Purple Saxifrage*

This is a low-growing spreading plant which has found its way into cultivation and has proved to be a very acceptable alpine. The distribution is quite widespread, but only in mountainous areas, from north to the south of Europe. It occurs in the Pyrenees at quite high altitudes, frequently encountered on rocky terrain near the high passes of Somport and Portale.

A mat forming species consisting of thin stems covered with tiny leaves arranged in opposite pairs, obovate to somewhat rounded generally overlapping, to 6mm long – the margins slightly hairy – dark-green in colour with 1-5 lime glands and set in 4 rows. Flowers about 1cm across, almost stalkless, pink or rich purple, borne at the tips of the stems. The petals nearly oval, the throat invariably a deeper shade.

Flowering is at its best between May and late August.

SEDUM anopetalum DC   (Crassulaceae)
   subsp. **montanum** Song. & Perr.

Common name — *Stonecrop*

A clustering plant closely related to *S. sediforme,* to about 9cm high, although the flowering stems far exceed this. Stems are decumbent, rooting at the nodes, the branches develop from near the top of the short stems – these with their close covering of leaves quickly form loose clusters. They are fairly widespread – in central and southern Spain, especially on low mountain slopes and rocky areas.

The leaves are about 1.2cm long, very succulent, greyish-green or dark-green, and directed upwards on the stems and branches where they are set opposite. They are rounded at the base, slightly pointed at the tip – the edges smooth. Flowering stems are to around 24cm long – sparsely leafy – bearing a more or less flattened head of many yellow flowers from 4 forked branchlets. It should be noted that the inflorescence is flattened not only in flower, but also in fruit. Flowering season is from June to early September.

SEDUM gypsicola Boiss. & Reut. (Crassulaceae)

Common name — *Grey-leaved Stonecrop*

A mat-forming species, perennial, evergreen and tending to flourish in rock crevices and the like, especially in limestone terrain on mountains at altitudes of 750-1000m in southern Spain, particularly towards the more westerly regions.

Plants spread freely by means of creeping, trailing stems and branches which root at the nodes – clumps rarely exceed 5cm high. Leaves arranged alternate, crowded near to the tips of the stems in five spiral rows, more or less elliptic with blunt tips, about 6mm long, greyish-green, occasionally tinged reddish. Flowers are borne terminally on the longer floral stems – several in a compact cluster. These are pure white and tipped pinkish on the sepals – star-like, about 6mm across – the sepals much smaller than the petals.

Flowers are to be seen during only a very limited period of the summer – principally in June to late July.

SEDUM sediforme (Jacq.) Pau   (Crassulaceae)

      Common name — *Stonecrop*

This is one of the several controversial species within the genus – it might well be termed *S. nicaeense* Allioni which appears to be totally synonymous. It is an evergreen, succulent plant with sturdy, fleshy stems and branches – in general it has a spreading habit. It is widespread in southern Spain, on hillsides and low mountain slopes, especially in the Mediterranean region.

Stems and branches can be up to 30cm or more long – the non-flowering branches covered around with glaucous or light green leaves – these are semi-elliptic, fleshy and pointed, to about 1.3cm long, set in a series of 'ranks'. Flowering stems are more or less erect, bearing a terminal head of pale greenish-yellow flowers – often flattish because of the very short horizontally-spreading branchlets – every branchlet bearing several small blooms, each about 1cm across.

Flowering is from June through into September.

SEMPERVIVUM arachnoideum L.   (Crassulaceae)

Common name — *Cobweb Houseleek*

One of the many dwarf succulent plants to be found in Spain. This is a mat-forming species and varies greatly according to habitat, inasmuch as several varieties and forms are botanically recorded. The accompanying picture was taken in the Pyrenees of eastern Spain, and is the type species.

The small greyish-green or deeper-green leaves are formed into a dense rosette 5-30mm in diameter, relatively globular in shape and covered completely with more or less densely tangled white cobweb-like hairs protruding from the tips of the individual leaves. The flowering stem is stout and firm, often to 30cm tall, covered with reddish scale-like leaves. Flowers are in a compact head, each flower 1-2.5cm across, rose-carmine, pink or rarely white in colour and star-like in appearance.

Flowering can be seen from late June until well into September.

SEMPERVIVUM montanum L.   (Crassulaceae)
subsp. **burnatii** Wettst.
Common name — *Mountain Houseleek*

This is one of a number of subspecies of *S. montanum*, all of which vary in minor characteristics. Just a few are Pyreneean plants, including this particular 'form' which seems to frequent fairly open ground, although stony, among coarse grasses and the like. The habitat is in the Sierre de S. Marcos near to Ripoll, but it is also known elsewhere at similar altitudes.

Leaves are a dull green, cuneate to oblanceolate, slightly sticky, minutely hairy margins – these form into a rosette which, when fully extended is about 15cm in diameter, although those observed are invariably scarcely semi-open. Plants do offset, but apparently not to the extent of many other species of *Sempervivum*. Flowers are borne on an erect, robust stem which is covered with pinkish, fleshy leaves – and a terminal head of several purplish-red star-like blooms.

Flowering is best seen from late June until September.

SERAPIAS cordigera L. (Orchidaceae)

Common name — *Heart-flowered Orchid*

A sturdy plant, generally found in small colonies, growing in moist areas near to the Mediterranean coast – near streams in grass and scrub or in open areas of moist woodland – prevalent in inland country behind Barcelona and nearer the coast of Costa Brava.

Plants grow to 15-35cm when reaching the flowering stage, sometimes even taller. Leaves are narrowly lanceolate, channelled and pointed – those at the base and sheathing the stem are, like the base of the stem, reddish-purple and red spotted. A spike carries up to 9-10 flowers – reddish-purple on the outer surface, rich violet within and a purplish or deep reddish lip – each flower about 3cm long. The lip is slightly hairy, the centre lobe cordate and pointed – and two blackish 'humps' in the throat, the side lobes are not easily observed being hidden by the petals and sepals which form the small hood.

Flowering is from March until early June.

SERAPIAS lingua L.   (Orchidaceae)

Common name — *Tongue Orchid*

A slender species which has quite a widespread distribution – being found in many European countries – it is well represented in the Mediterranean region of Spain – in woodlands and scrub country, particularly in moist grassy places near to coast.

Plants are to a matter of 25cm tall, more often considerably shorter. Leaves are narrowly lance-shaped, glaucous – keeled and pointed, the sheathing leaves at the base of the stem are fresh-green. Bracts about 2cm long, suffused purple. Spike 6-9cm long, usually 2-6 flowered, these set well apart – each flower 1-3cm long. The sepals are purplish, often green speckled and forming a hood – the lip 3-lobed, the centre longer and tongue-like, generally red or purplish – the side lobes purple, and there is a single blackish 'hump' at the base of the lip and difficult to see due to its position.

Flowers are to be seen from March to mid-June.

SOLANUM sodomeum L. (Solanaceae)

Common name — *Nightshade*

Sometimes referred to as the False Sodom Apple. It is an African species which has become widely distributed throughout much of the Mediterranean region. It is a prickly plant which can reach 1m or more high, frequenting more westerly parts of Spain, in open grassy areas, in hedgerows and sandy places, particularly in the Provinces of Granada and Malaga.

Both the tall stem and branches are covered with sharp yellowish spines. The leaves also are spiny, the undersurface more so than the upper – they tend to be undulating which emphasises the deeply lobed margins of the foliage. Flowers are large, about 2.5cm across, pinkish-purple, shortly tubular, with the lobes spreading and becoming almost recurved – the calyx is also spiny, whilst the corolla is minutely hairy. Fruits are a bright yellow, almost circular, about 2cm across. A summer flowering species – especially between June and late August.

SPARTIUM junceum L.   (Leguminosae)

Common name — *Spanish Broom*

A large, few-leaved shrub often attaining over 2m tall and presenting a truly magnificent plant when in full flower. It is well distributed throughout the Mediterranean region, frequenting dry hills and wooded areas – common in the maquis and generally growing in quite calcareous soils.

An erect, often unruly plant which has almost leafless cylindrical, rush-like stems. Leaves are few, narrowly lanceolate and small and they soon fall. Flowers are quite large, 2-2.5cm long with a distinctive rounded standard, and also a pointed keel – they are sweetly scented, deep bright yellow in colour and borne in stiff or lax terminal spikes. Large pea-like seed pods follow – about 6cm or more long and 7mm wide becoming black as they ripen – contains several seeds.

Flowering period extends from May until late August. The dried stems are used extensively for basket making by local craftsmen.

TUSSILAGO farfara L.   (Compositae)

Common name — *Coltsfoot*

This well-known perennial plant is very much in evidence in Britain as it is in many parts of Europe including Spain. It is an attractive, clump-forming species which in some parts is considered almost a weed – but it possesses a charm which makes it a very noticeable plant. It is to be found in more northerly and central areas of the country in moist parts, near riversides and ditches.

The rootstock consists of a deep-set rhizome from which arise sturdy, scaly stems in early spring, these to about 15cm tall. Leaves appear after the flower-stem, and are more or less rounded, white-felted on the underside. Flowers are solitary, borne terminally, about 3cm diameter consisting of numerous extremely slender ray florets of bright yellow – the stem also develops small fleshy leaves set alternate.

The flowering season extends from February until early May.

VINCA difformis Pour. (Apocynaceae)

Common name — *Intermediate Periwinkle*

An evergreen trailing plant with similar characteristics as others of the genus. It is, perhaps, less common than other species, yet notwithstanding, has quite a widespread distribution in the Mediterranean region, also to a lesser degree in the Galicia Province. It is found in shaded places, in uncultivated areas where it is generally moist, beside streams, ditches and the like.

Leaves are totally hairless, oval-lanceolate, rounded at the base, not heart-shaped as occurs with some other species, pointed at the tips, and set opposite along the slender stems. Flowers are solitary, borne from the axils of the leaves, 3-4cm across – the petals hairless, more or less oval in shape, pointed at the tips and narrowing towards the base – a pale-blue or lilac-blue, and they are short-stalked.

Flowering can continue over quite a long period, dependent upon habitat – from early February to late May.

VIOLA tricolor L.   (Violaceae)

Common name — *Wild Pansy*

This really requires no introduction as it is quite well-known in Britain as well as elsewhere in Europe. It is a perennial, be it only short-lived – although often it seems to be an annual which propagates itself readily. One of the choicest of pansies – a parent of many of the popular garden varieties. It is to be seen in grassy meadows on quite high ground in the Pyrenees, but also encountered at much lower levels in north, central and more southerly parts of Spain.

More or less tufted plants, rarely exceeding 15cm tall when in flower. Stems are soft, erect or decumbent, bearing ovate-lanceolate leaves about 5cm long, often crenated so as to form segments, other times entire. Flowers are variable, either violet or yellow with conspicuous streaks, to about 2.5cm wide and borne terminally on slender stems.

The flowering season can prove quite lengthy – from late March (dependent upon habitat) to late September.

INDEX